MARVEL

WHAT WOULD

THE MIGHTY THOR

DO?

A STUDIO PRESS BOOK

First published in the UK in 2021 by Studio Press,
an imprint of Bonnier Books UK Limited,
4th Floor, Victoria House, Bloomsbury Square, London, WC1B 4DA
Owned by Bonnier Books,
Sveavägen 56, Stockholm, Sweden

www.bonnierbooks.co.uk

© 2021 MARVEL

1 3 5 7 9 10 8 6 4 2

ISBN 978-1-80078-086-6

Written by Susie Rae
Edited by Saaleh Patel and Sophie Blackman
Designed by Rob Ward
Production by Emma Kidd

A CIP catalogue for this book is available from the British Library

Printed and bound in Italy

... ONE SHOULD FIRST MAKE ABSOLUTELY SURE THAT THE BEAST IS NOT, IN FACT, YOUR ADOPTED BROTHER IN DISGUISE. AGAIN.

ORDERING A COFFEE...
ONE MUST BEAR IN MIND THAT THE GOBLETS MORTALS USE FOR THEIR MORNING BEVERAGES ARE, IN FACT, REUSABLE.
IT IS CONSIDERED IMPOLITE TO BREAK SAID GOBLET, NO MATTER HOW DELICIOUS THE DRINK IS. A SIMPLE 'THANK YOU' WILL SUFFICE.

DEAD PHONE BATTERY...

I ONCE TRIED CHANNELLING LIGHTNING FROM THE HEAVENS TO REVIVE MY GOOD FRIEND STARK'S PORTABLE COMMUNICATION DEVICE WHEN IT EXPIRED...

... BUT IT DID NOT WORK, AND HE HAS ASKED ME TO REFRAIN FROM TRYING THAT AGAIN IN FUTURE. APPARENTLY, THE THING TO DO IS SIMPLY ASK A FRIEND FOR THEIRS INSTEAD.

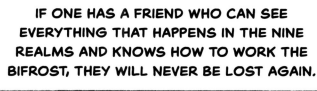

IF ONE HAS A FRIEND WHO CAN SEE EVERYTHING THAT HAPPENS IN THE NINE REALMS AND KNOWS HOW TO WORK THE BIFROST, THEY WILL NEVER BE LOST AGAIN.

REALLY, MORE PEOPLE SHOULD BECOME FRIENDS WITH HEIMDALL. HE IS VERY NICE.

DISAGREEMENTS WITH SIBLINGS...

WHO DOES NOT FIGHT WITH THEIR SIBLINGS? ESPECIALLY WHEN SAID SIBLING LIKES TO SHAPESHIFT INTO DIFFERENT FORMS TO TRICK ME, OR OCCASIONALLY TRIES TO TAKE OVER THE UNIVERSE.

NONETHELESS, I LOVE MY FAMILY MEMBERS AND USUALLY TRY TO KEEP THE PEACE. I JUST ALSO KEEP AN EYE ON THEM TO MAKE SURE THEY DON'T TRY TO USURP THE THRONE... AGAIN.

SELF-WORTH...

EVERYONE, NO MATTER
WHO THEY ARE, IS WORTHY.
THEY MAY NOT BE WORTHY OF
SOMETHING AS ILLUSTRIOUS AS
WIELDING THE GREAT MJÖLNIR,
WEAPON OF THE GODS...

... BUT THEY ARE STILL
WORTHY OF SOMETHING.
A NEW PAIR OF BOOTS, PERHAPS.

HEALTHY EATING...

WE SHOULD TREAT OUR BODIES
AS ONE WOULD A TEMPLE.
I FEAST UPON THE GOLDEN
APPLES OF IDUUN TO KEEP MY
BODY HEALTHY AND POWERFUL.

REGULAR MIDGARDIAN APPLES
MAY NOT KEEP MORTALS ALIVE
FOR THOUSANDS OF YEARS,
BUT THEY WILL STOP SCURVY.

BEING ASSERTIVE...

THE BEST WAY TO ASSERT
ONESELF IN A CONVERSATION,
I HAVE FOUND, IS TO WIELD A
MAGNIFICENT URU HAMMER
TO INTIMIDATE ENEMIES.

IF THAT IS IMPOSSIBLE, THEN GLOWERING
SLIGHTLY LETS OPPONENTS KNOW
THAT ONE MEANS BUSINESS.

FORGETFULNESS...

WHEN THE FATE OF THE WORLD IS HIGH ON ONE'S LIST OF CONCERNS, IT IS EASY TO FORGET TRIVIAL THINGS LIKE NAMES.

GIVING FRIENDS COLLECTIVE NAMES, LIKE THE AVENGERS OR THE WARRIORS THREE, WILL MAKE THEM MUCH EASIER TO REMEMBER.

BAD WEATHER...

AS THE GOD OF THUNDER, I AM SOMEWHAT OF AN EXPERT IN THIS FIELD.

MANY MORTALS WILL STAY INDOORS DURING STORMY WEATHER, BUT I SAY, EMBRACE IT! CHANNEL THE POWER OF THE STORM TO ACHIEVE GOALS...

... A TRUE HERO DOES NOT ALLOW THEMSELVES TO BE STOPPED BY SOMETHING AS MINOR AS A BIT OF RAIN.

DIFFERENCES OF OPINION...

EVERYONE HAS THEIR OWN OPINIONS. FOR EXAMPLE, HULK BELIEVES THAT HE IS THE STRONGEST AVENGER AND I KNOW THAT, CLEARLY, HE IS NOT, FOR I AM THE STRONGEST AVENGER...

... HOWEVER, ONE MUST RESPECT THE OPINIONS OF OTHERS, NO MATTER HOW WRONG OR FOOLISH THOSE OPINIONS MAY BE.

STILL, I AM ALWAYS PREPARED TO PARTAKE IN A SMALL, FRIENDLY BATTLE TO DEFEND MY — CORRECT — OPINION, IF NEED BE.

FASHION...

WEAR A CAPE. WEAR ARMOUR. WIELD
A MAGNIFICENT SIGNATURE WEAPON.
THIS IS THE PINNACLE OF DRESS
IN EVERY SINGLE REALM.

MAKING BREAKFAST...

AFTER A MINOR INCIDENT WHICH RESULTED IN A FIRE IN AVENGERS' TOWER, I HAVE CHOSEN TO STOP BOILING WATER FOR MY MORNING BEVERAGE BY SUMMONING A BOLT OF LIGHTNING.

AS STARK WAS KIND ENOUGH TO POINT OUT, THERE ARE DEVICES CALLED 'KETTLES' THAT WILL DO THIS INSTEAD.

HOME...

I HAVE LEARNED, IN MY TIME,
THAT HOME IS NOT A PLACE.
IT IS THE PEOPLE THAT YOU LOVE.
REMEMBER THAT, AND IT WILL
GET YOU THROUGH NEARLY
ANYTHING, EVEN IF YOU
KEEP GETTING EXILED.

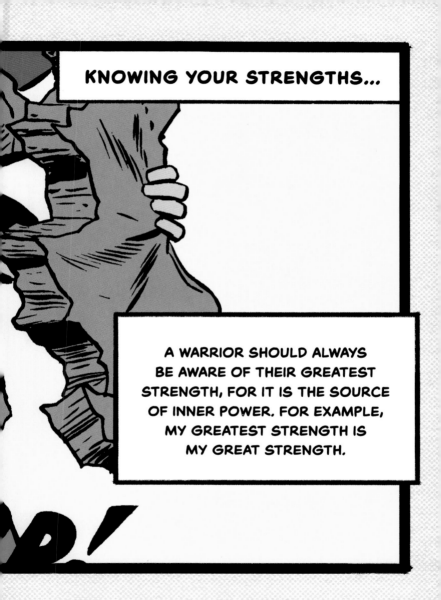

CATCHING A COLD...

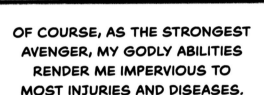

OF COURSE, AS THE STRONGEST AVENGER, MY GODLY ABILITIES RENDER ME IMPERVIOUS TO MOST INJURIES AND DISEASES.

AS MORTALS ARE NOT SO BLESSED, THEY SHOULD INSIST ON BEING BROUGHT FLAGONS OF CHICKEN SOUP UNTIL THEIR WEAK MORTAL BODIES RECOVER FROM THEIR AFFLICTIONS.

TAKING THINGS LITERALLY...

WHEN SOMEONE SAYS, 'BRING THE THUNDER', THIS MEANS THAT THEY WANT ONE TO PERFORM A TASK WITH ENTHUSIASM...

... AND WHEN SOMEONE APOLOGISES FOR 'STEALING YOUR THUNDER', THEY ARE TALKING ABOUT TAKING CREDIT FOR AN IDEA. THEY DO NOT MEAN THESE THINGS LITERALLY, AS I HAVE LEARNED.

DEALING WITH FAILURE...

A WARRIOR MUST LEARN TO
ACCEPT DEFEAT GRACIOUSLY,
NOBODY LIKES A THOR LOSER.

MY BROTHER HAS TRIED TO TAKE OVER THE WORLD AND USURP OUR FATHER'S THRONE SEVERAL TIMES...

... WHILE I HAVEN'T ATTEMPTED TO TAKE OVER THE WORLD ONCE.

REGARDLESS, WE MUST EMBRACE OUR DIFFERENCES AND ENJOY THE THINGS THAT WE DO HAVE IN COMMON. FOR EXAMPLE...

... NEITHER MY SIBLINGS NOR I UNDERSTAND HOW MIDGARDIAN PORTABLE COMMUNICATION DEVICES WORK AT ALL, WHICH BONDS US.

NO DINNER PARTY IS COMPLETE WITHOUT THE HEARTIEST OF FOODS AND THE STRONGEST OF ALES...

... THIS WILL GIVE GUESTS THE ENERGY REQUIRED FOR A GOOD POST-DINNER BRAWL — THE MOST IMPORTANT PART OF ANY SOCIAL GATHERING.

STARTING A RELATIONSHIP...

MATTERS OF LOVE ARE MUCH LIKE
WIELDING THE GREAT MJÖLNIR —
ONE SHOULD ONLY ENTER
INTO A RELATIONSHIP WITH
SOMEONE WHO IS WORTHY.

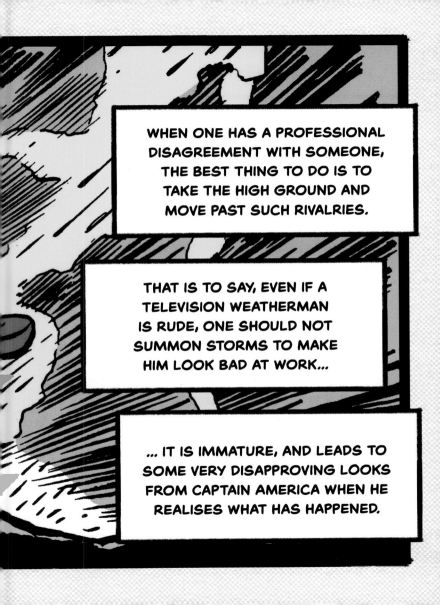

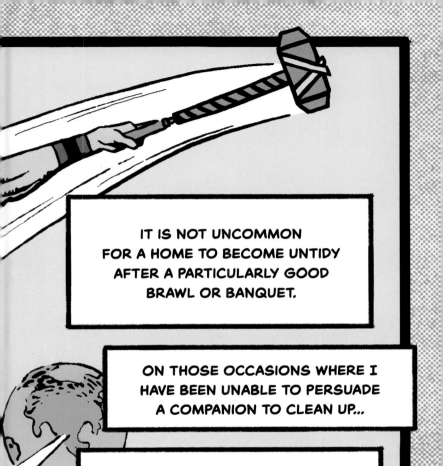

ASPIRATIONS...

NEVER LET ANYBODY SAY THAT DREAMS ARE NOT ACHIEVABLE. WHEN I WAS A YOUNGSTER, I ALWAYS DREAMED OF GREATNESS...

... AND YES, I HAVE STOPPED THE UNIVERSE FROM BEING DESTROYED BY HORDES OF VILLAINS SEVERAL TIMES...

... BUT MORE IMPORTANTLY, I HAVE WORKED OUT HOW TO MAKE THE MICROWAVE IN AVENGERS TOWER WORK, WHICH IS MY GREATEST ACHIEVEMENT TO DATE.

OTHER MARVEL BOOKS...

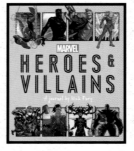